EXTRAORDINARY
X-MEN

PURPORTED TO BE THE NEXT STAGE IN HUMAN EVOLUTION, MUTANTS MANIFEST SUPERHUMAN POWERS AND ABILITIES UPON REACHING ADOLESCENCE. BUT RATHER THAN BEING CELEBRATED FOR THEIR GIFTS, MUTANTS ARE HATED AND FEARED. WITH THE FATE OF THEIR RACE HANGING IN THE BALANCE, MUTANTKIND NEEDS HEROES WHO WILL LEAD THEM INTO THE FUTURE. MUTANTKIND NEEDS...

THOUSANDS OF YEARS IN THE FUTURE, THE X-MEN WERE CONFRONTED BY THEIR WORST FEARS MANIFEST: THE WORLD HAD BEEN REMADE IN THE IMAGE OF THEIR LONGTIME ADVERSARY APOCALYPSE, AND ONE OF THEIR OWN, COLOSSUS, WAS TRANSFORMED INTO HIS HORSEMAN OF WAR. AND TO MAKE MATTERS WORSE, MAGIK LEARNED THAT THE X-MEN'S NEWEST CHARGE, SAPNA, WAS CORRUPTED BY HER OWN POWER. WHILE THE X-MEN WERE ABLE TO ESCAPE THE DYSTOPIC EARTH AND RETURN TO THE PRESENT, THEY WERE FORCED TO BRING APOCALYPSE WITH THEM, AS HE WAS THEIR ONLY HOPE OF RESTORING COLOSSUS. BUT COLOSSUS ESCAPED, LEAVING THE X-MEN SCRAMBLING TO FIND HIM AND PREVENT THAT DARK FUTURE FROM COMING TO PASS...

COLLECTION EDITOR: JENNIFER GRÜNWALD
ASSISTANT EDITOR: CAITLIN O'CONNELL
ASSOCIATE MANAGING EDITOR: KATERI WOODY
EDITOR, SPECIAL PROJECTS: MARK D. BEAZLEY

VP PRODUCTION & SPECIAL PROJECTS: JEFF YOUNGQUIST
SVP PRINT, SALES & MARKETING: DAVID GABRIEL
BOOK DESIGNER: JAY BOWEN

EDITOR IN CHIEF: AXEL ALONSO
CHIEF CREATIVE OFFICER: JOE QUESADA
PUBLISHER: DAN BUCKLEY
EXECUTIVE PRODUCER: ALAN FINE

EXTRAORDINARY X-MEN VOL. 3: KINGDOMS FALL. Contains material originally published in magazine form as EXTRAORDINARY X-MEN #13-16 and ANNUAL #1. First printing 2017. ISBN# 978-0-7851-9936-6. Published by MARVEL WORLDWIDE, INC., a subsidiary of MARVEL ENTERTAINMENT, LLC. OFFICE OF PUBLICATION: 135 West 50th Street, New York, NY 10020. **Printed in Canada.** ALAN FINE, President, Marvel Entertainment; DAN BUCKLEY, President, TV, Publishing & Brand Management; JOE QUESADA, Chief Creative Officer; TOM BREVOORT, SVP of Publishing; DAVID BOGART, SVP of Business Affairs & Operations, Publishing & Partnership; C.B. CEBULSKI, VP of Brand Management & Development, Asia; DAVID GABRIEL, SVP of Sales & Marketing, Publishing; JEFF YOUNGQUIST, VP of Production & Special Projects; DAN CARR, Executive Director of Publishing Technology; ALEX MORALES, Director of Publishing Operations; SUSAN CRESPI, Production Manager; STAN LEE, Chairman Emeritus. For information regarding advertising in Marvel Comics or on Marvel.com, please contact Vit DeBellis, Integrated Sales Manager, at vdebellis@marvel.com. For Marvel subscription inquiries, please call 888-511-5480. **Manufactured between 12/23/2016 and 1/30/2017 by SOLISCO PRINTERS, SCOTT, QC, CANADA.**

10 9 8 7 6 5 4 3 2 1

KINGDOMS FALL

JEFF LEMIRE
WRITER

VICTOR IBAÑEZ
ARTIST

GUILLERMO MOGORRÓN
LAYOUT ARTIST, #14-15

JAY DAVID RAMOS
COLOR ARTIST

VC's JOE CARAMAGNA
LETTERER

HUMBERTO RAMOS & EDGAR DELGADO (#13-15)
AND KEN LASHLEY & NOLAN WOODARD (#16)
COVER ARTISTS

CHRIS ROBINSON
ASSISTANT EDITOR

DANIEL KETCHUM
EDITOR

MARK PANICCIA
X-MEN GROUP EDITOR

ANNUAL #1

"PRISON BREAK"

OLLIE MASTERS
WRITER

CARLO BARBERI
PENCILER

WALDEN WONG
INKER

ISRAEL SILVA WITH
RACHELLE ROSENBERG
COLOR ARTISTS

MARK BASSO
EDITOR

DANIEL KETCHUM
CONSULTING EDITOR

"FORGE, WE HAVE A PROBLEM"

BRANDON MONTCLARE
WRITER

ROSI KÄMPE
ARTIST

IAN HERRING
COLORIST

CHRIS ROBINSON
EDITOR

VC's JOE CARAMAGNA
LETTERER

VICTOR IBAÑEZ & JOSÉ VILLARRUBIA
COVER ART

MARK PANICCIA
X-MEN GROUP EDITOR

X-MEN CREATED BY STAN LEE & JACK KIRBY

13

LIMBO.
SHOW ME!

I'VE GOT HER!
DID YOU FIND HER, ILLYANA? DID YOU FIND SAPNA?
NO, STORM, BUT HER SPECTRAL TRAIL IS STILL FRESH.
ALL I HAVE TO DO IS FOLLOW!
BOOGERS!
EXCUSE ME?
WHIMPER
SAPNA'S PET DEMON.
HEY, BOY. YOU MISS HER TOO, HUH?
WHIMPER

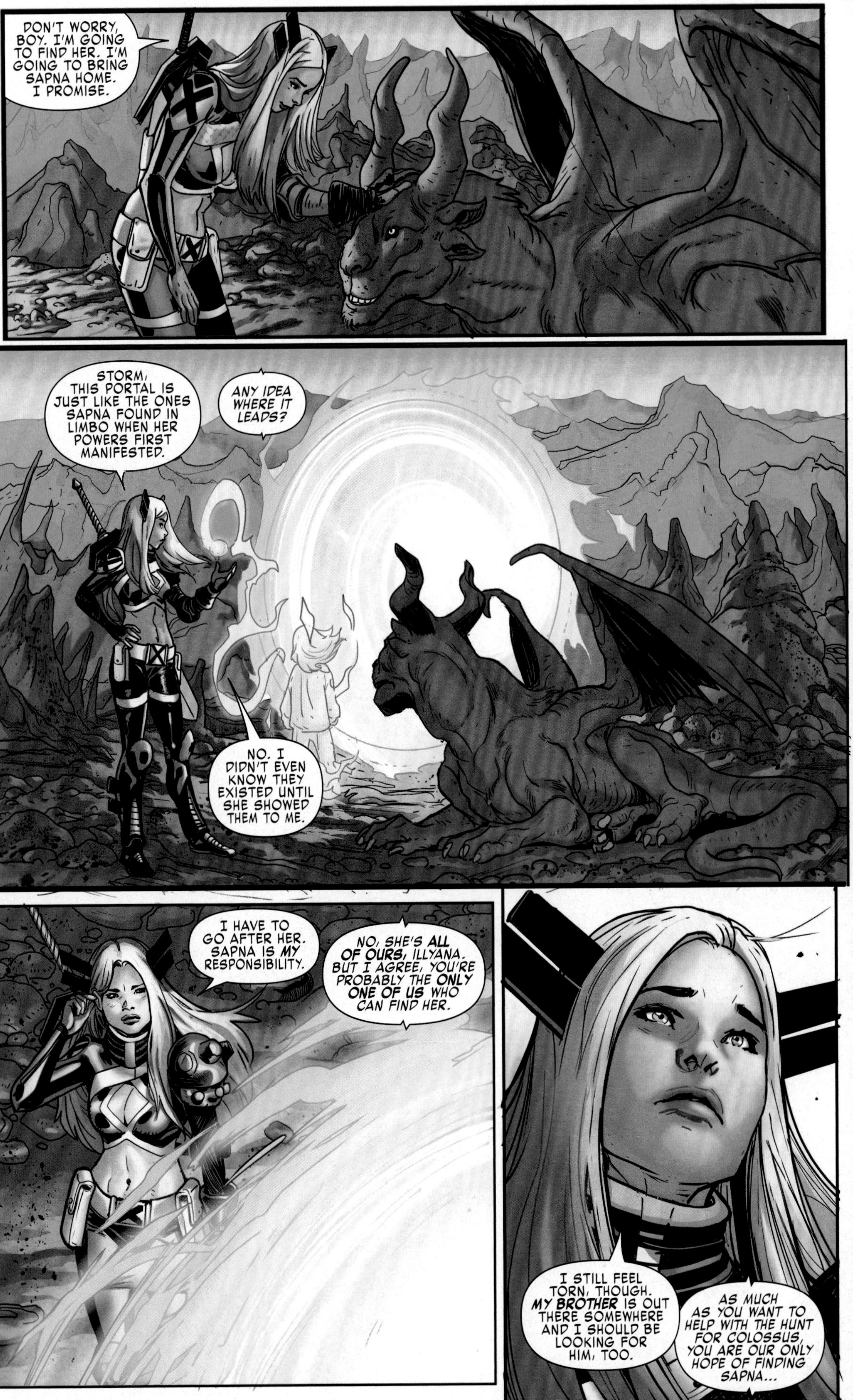

STORM, THIS PORTAL IS JUST LIKE THE ONES SAPNA FOUND IN LIMBO WHEN HER POWERS FIRST MANIFESTED.
ANY IDEA WHERE IT LEADS?
NO. I DIDN'T EVEN KNOW THEY EXISTED UNTIL SHE SHOWED THEM TO ME.

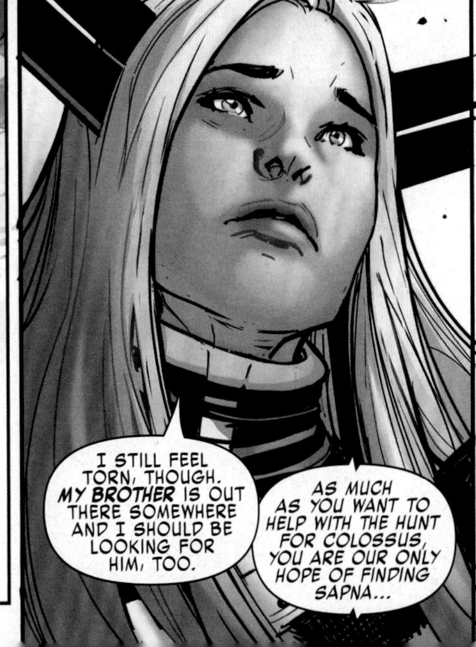

...WE HAVE THINGS COVERED HERE.
DO WE?
KEEPING HIM IN X-HAVEN IS REALLY GIVING ME THE CREEPS.
APOCALYPSE IS NOT GOING ANYWHERE, JEAN. I BUILT THIS CELL SPECIFICALLY TO HOLD HIM.
NOW, LET'S JUST HOPE I CAN USE HIM TO FIGURE OUT A WAY TO TRANSFORM COLOSSUS BACK TO NORMAL.
FIRST WE HAVE TO FIND PIOTR.
DON'T WORRY ABOUT THAT, 'RO...

"...WE GOT TWO OF OUR BEST ON THE HUNT."
PRAGUE.
HURRY UP. IT'S DAMP IN HERE AND I THINK I'M GETTING A COLD.
WOULD YOU QUIT COMPLAINING? ALL YOU DO IS COMPLAIN. YOU ARE NEVER GOING TO BE INITIATED INTO CLAN AKKABA IF YOU WHINE LIKE THIS ALL THE TIME.
WELL, THESE ROBES ARE TOO THIN. AKKABA NEEDS TO DESIGN SOMETHING WARMER FOR US TO WEAR.
WHEN THE MASTER APOCALYPSE IS FREED WE WILL ALL BASK IN THE WARMTH OF HIS POWER.
YEAH, YEAH...
BAMF
OH, &$%#!
MUTANT! RUN!
THERE IS NOWHERE LEFT TO RUN, HEATHENS.
BAMF
I AM EVERYWHERE.
K-KILL HIM!

DID I JUST HEAR YOU COMPLAINING ABOUT ***THE COLD?***
GAH!
'CAUSE YOU AIN'T SEEN NOTHING YET.
I THINK YOUR SENSE OF HUMOR IS GETTING WORSE, BOBBY.

AT LEAST I HAVE ONE, ELF.
ONLY LOGAN GETS TO CALL ME THAT.
--UNGH!
WE WANT COLOSSUS!
APOCALYPSE WILL WIPE YOU ALL FROM THE FACE OF THE EARTH! HE WILL MAKE THIS WORLD PURE. DO WHAT YOU WANT TO ME, IT WILL CHANGE NOTHING! I WILL DIE FOR HIM!
I THINK IT IS TIME TO TEST THOSE CONVICTIONS...

I WILL BLEED YOU LIKE THE PIG YOU ARE!
W-WE DON'T KNOW ANYTHING! WE AREN'T EVEN FULL AKKABA YET. JUST PLEDGES. THEY ALL PICKED UP AND LEFT A DAY AGO. I DON'T KNOW WHERE THEY WENT. WE--
UUR!
NO! PLEASE! I SWEAR!
KURT.
LOOK AT THEM, THEY'RE SCARED OUT OF THEIR MINDS. THEY DON'T KNOW ANYTHING, AND EVEN IF THEY DID, KILLING THEM ISN'T GOING TO GET US ANY ANSWERS. THAT'S NOT WHO WE ARE.
WHAT?! THESE MEN ARE CLAN AKKABA, THE WORSHIPPERS OF APOCALYPSE. IF ANYONE KNOWS WHERE COLOSSUS IS, IT IS THEM!
LOOK AROUND, BOBBY. TIMES HAVE CHANGED. WE CANNOT AFFORD TO BE WEAK ANY LONGER.
BEING TRUE TO OURSELVES IS NEVER WEAK.
LOOK, WE'LL FIND PETE, I KNOW WE WILL. STORM WAS ABLE TO CONVINCE S.H.I.E.L.D. TO HELP US OUT. THEY GAVE US ALL THEIR INTEL ON CLAN AKKABA, INCLUDING THE LOCATIONS OF ALL THEIR KNOWN CELLS. THIS IS ONLY OUR FIRST STOP.
LOOK, I KNOW YOU'VE BEEN THROUGH A LOT. ARE YOU SURE YOU'RE GOOD?
YES. I--THANK YOU, BOBBY.
WHAT ABOUT THESE TWO?
LET'S PUT THEM ON ICE.
YOU NEED TO STOP.
I KNOW, I KNOW...
BAMF

LIMBO.
OKAY, STORM, THERE'S NO TELLING HOW STABLE THIS PORTAL IS. I'M GOING IN.

NOT ALONE YOU'RE NOT.
AH!
WHAT ARE YOU DOING CREEPING UP ON ME LIKE THAT?!
I DIDN'T THINK YOU OF ALL PEOPLE WOULD SCARE SO EASILY, ILLYANA.

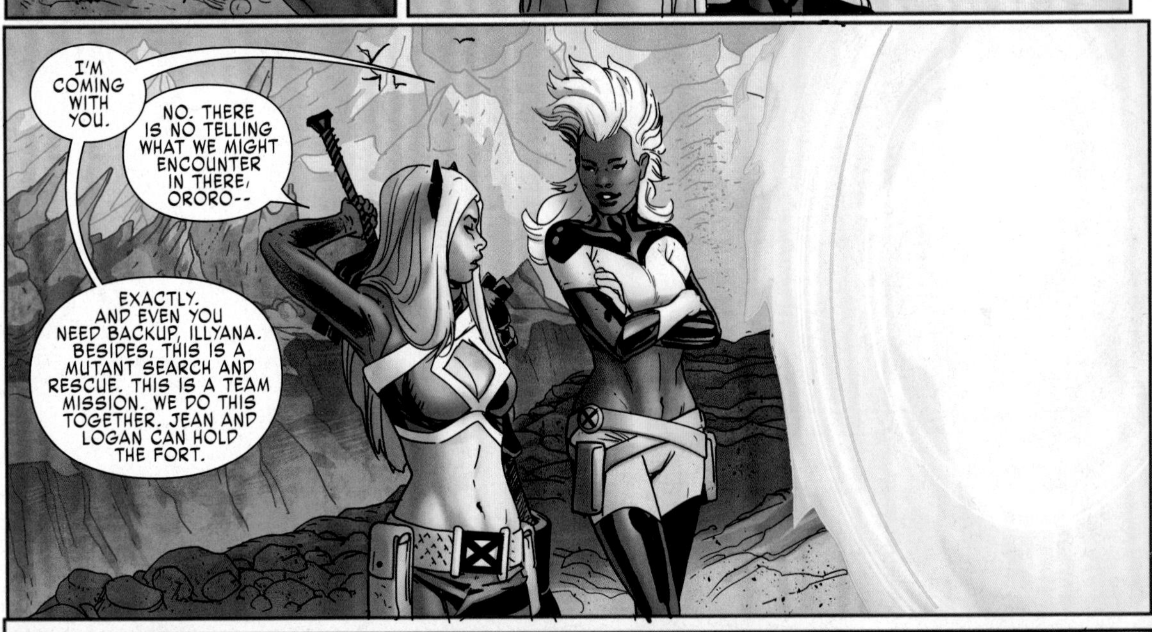
I'M COMING WITH YOU.
NO. THERE IS NO TELLING WHAT WE MIGHT ENCOUNTER IN THERE, ORORO--
EXACTLY. AND EVEN YOU NEED BACKUP, ILLYANA. BESIDES, THIS IS A MUTANT SEARCH AND RESCUE. THIS IS A TEAM MISSION. WE DO THIS TOGETHER. JEAN AND LOGAN CAN HOLD THE FORT.

SMART GIRL.
YOU ARE THE ONLY PERSON I HAVE EVER MET MORE STUBBORN THAN ME.

BE READY FOR ANYTHING.
I AM. ARE YOU?
ALWAYS.

GODDESS!
IT SEEMS THESE WORLDS ONCE HAD MANY GODS, STORM.
WHAT ARE THESE PLACES, ILLYANA?

I DO NOT KNOW FOR SURE. DIFFERENT REALMS, OR WHAT'S LEFT OF THEM. ALL CONNECTED BY THESE PORTALS. BUT SAPNA IS NOT HERE. WE MUST KEEP GOING!
WHERE?
THERE! HOLD ON!

--UNGH!
IS THIS THE PLACE? IS SHE HERE?
I-I'M NOT SURE. SOMEONE IS HERE. I'M PICKING UP SOME STRANGE ENERGY, FOR SURE.
I HATE TO THINK OF SAPNA ALONE IN THIS WORLD. IF SHE IS HERE, SHE MAY BE THE ONLY THING LEFT ALIVE.
YOU SHOULD BE SO LUCKY, LOVE.
WHAT?!

ARRGH!
I DON'T KNOW WHO YOU ARE, BUT YOU MADE ONE HELL OF A BLOODY MISTAKE COMING TO MY WORLD.

WHERE IS SHE?! WHERE IS SAPNA?!
YOU HAVE ANY IDEA WHAT THE GOTH QUEEN IS TALKING ABOUT, ANNE TENNA?
NONE, JACK CRAW. BUT THEY'RE AGENTS OF THE WORLD-EATER. MY SENSORS ARE PICKING UP SOME BAD MAGIC ON THEM!
YOU HEARD HER! SPECTRA, ENOCH, KILL THEM!

X-HAVEN.
UM...MR. FORGE, MR. LOGAN...
CAN I DO ANYTHING TO HELP?
ERNST?! YOU HAVE A CONCUSSION AND A BROKEN COLLARBONE, YOU SHOULD NOT BE OUT OF BED. YOU--YOU'RE JUST GOING TO GET IN THE WAY DOWN HERE. I HAVE TOO MUCH WORK TO DO TO WORRY ABOUT YOU RIGHT NOW.
CRIPES, FORGE, YOU COULD'A TAKEN IT A BIT EASIER ON THE KID! SHE WAS JUST TRYING TO HELP.
HELP?! AND HOW COULD ERNST HAVE HELPED ME, LOGAN? CEREBRA IS IN PIECES. I HAD TO DOWNLOAD HER A.I. INTO THE COMPUTER UNTIL I HAVE TIME TO GET TO REPAIRING HER BODY--
HELLO! I'M RIGHT HERE, DID SOMEONE MENTION MY NAME? CAN I BE OF ASSISTANCE?
NO!

AND ON TOP OF THAT, I HAVE TO TRY AND REVERSE ENGINEER APOCALYPSE'S POWER TO TRY AND FIND A CURE FOR COLOSSUS!
AND WHILE I'M ON THE TOPIC, WHAT ARE YOU DOING DOWN HERE?! NO OFFENSE, BUT YOUR SUPERIOR INTELLECT ISN'T EXACTLY AN ASSET RIGHT NOW! WHY DON'T YOU GO FIND SOMETHING TO SCRATCH!
SO, I'M SORRY, LOGAN, BUT I DON'T HAVE TIME TO BE POLITE RIGHT NOW! ESPECIALLY NOT TO YOU!
LOGAN?! WHERE'S THE FIRE?
YOU DON'T WANNA GO IN THERE, JEANNIE. TRUST ME. FORGE HAS HIS WIRES IN A BUNCH.
UH-HUH, AND THAT WOULDN'T HAVE ANYTHING TO DO WITH YOU, WOULD IT?
OH, COME ON, LOGAN, I WAS JUST--
OH, GO POKE AROUND IN SOMEONE ELSE'S HEAD, WOULD YA?!
WHATEVER. GRUMPY OLD... GRUMP!

AL-QASR, EGYPT.
BAMF
GOD, I HATE THAT! YOUR BRIMSTONE MAKES ME MELT.
SOMETHING'S NOT RIGHT HERE. THIS PLACE SEEMS ABANDONED.
YES, AND I THINK I HEARD--
BRAT-AT-AT-AT AT-AT-AT AT-AT-AT
YEP, I'D SAY THIS IS THE RIGHT PLACE.
I'VE GOT THEM.
BAMF
BAMF

WHERE IS HE?! WHERE IS COLOSSUS?
UH... KURT.
I THINK WE FOUND SOMETHING.

BE CAREFUL, BOBBY...
"...THERE'S NO TELLING WHAT MIGHT BE DOWN HERE."
HOLD HER STILL, ENOCH! I'LL TAKE CONTROL OF HER!
ARRRRGHH!
WHOA.
MEIN GOTT!
ARRRGH!
SHRACK!

IT'S US, KURT. IT'S EVERYTHING THAT'S HAPPENED.
OR EVERYTHING THAT WILL HAPPEN.

14

EGYPT.
YOU DON'T REALLY THINK THESE AKKABA GUYS CAN SEE THE FUTURE, DO YOU, KURT?
NOTHING SURPRISES ME ANYMORE, BOBBY. WITH ALL WE'VE BEEN THROUGH--
KURT?
KURT, IS THAT YOU?
PIOTR?!
KURT, I--I NEED HELP...
I AM HERE, MY FRIEND!
KURT, WAIT!

YOUR BLIND FAITH ALWAYS WAS YOUR GREATEST WEAKNESS.
KURT!
THOOM!
UNGH!

GET AWAY FROM HIM, PETE!
PLEASE.
CHAK!
BETTER TO STAY DOWN, BOBBY. YOU ARE OUT OF YOUR LEAGUE.
GUH!
YOU SHOULD NEVER HAVE COME HERE, KURT. I WOULD HAVE PREFERRED IT NOT BE YOU. LOGAN OR JEAN PERHAPS, BUT NOT *YOU*.
UNFORTUNATELY, I HAVE *NO CHOICE*.

ELSEWHERE.
BLAST HER AGAIN, SPECTRA! USE THE WEATHER WITCH'S POWER FOR ALL IT'S WORTH!
QUIET, JACK CRAW... CONTROLLING HER POWER REQUIRES MUCH CONCENTRATION.
I'M ONLY GOING TO WARN YOU ONCE, GHOST WOMAN. GET OUT OF MY FRIEND OR I WILL DESTROY YOU!
I CAN SEE WHY THE WORLD EATER WAS DRAWN TO YOU. YOUR SOUL IS BLACK. I SEE IT IN YOUR EYES.

WRONG ANSWER.
GAAAAHH!
UNGH!
WELL, WELL, AREN'T YOU A SAUCY LITTLE MINX.
I WANT THE BLONDE ONE.
ALL YOURS, ENOCH.
WE ARE LOOKING FOR A LOST CHILD! WE KNOW NOTHING ABOUT THIS "WORLD EATER."
SHRACK!
LIAR! YOU ARE BOTH HIS WORMS! WE'VE SEEN YOUR KIND BEFORE! IT'S SCUM LIKE YOU WHO TORE THE LATTICE APART IN THE FIRST PLACE!
THE LATTICE? IS THAT WHAT THIS PLACE IS?
QUIET, INTERLOPER! THE WORLD EATER'S POISON SEEPS FROM YER LIPS!

DON'T LET THEM SPEAK! THE MORE THEY TALK, THE MORE THE EATER GETS HIS HOOKS IN YOU!
KZZZAT!
ILLYANA, THEY WON'T LISTEN TO REASON! DO YOU SENSE SAPNA ANYWHERE NEAR THIS PLACE?!
NO, I DON'T.
HER TRAIL KEEPS GOING THROUGH THE NEXT PORTAL, BUT IT'S FADING FAST. IF WE DON'T GET OUT OF HERE AND KEEP FOLLOWING, I'M GOING TO LOSE IT ALTOGETHER.
STAY CLOSE, ILLYANA!
WHAT ARE YOU GOING TO DO, STORM?

SHOW THEM WHAT A "WEATHER WITCH" REALLY IS.
THAT WAY! *HURRY!*

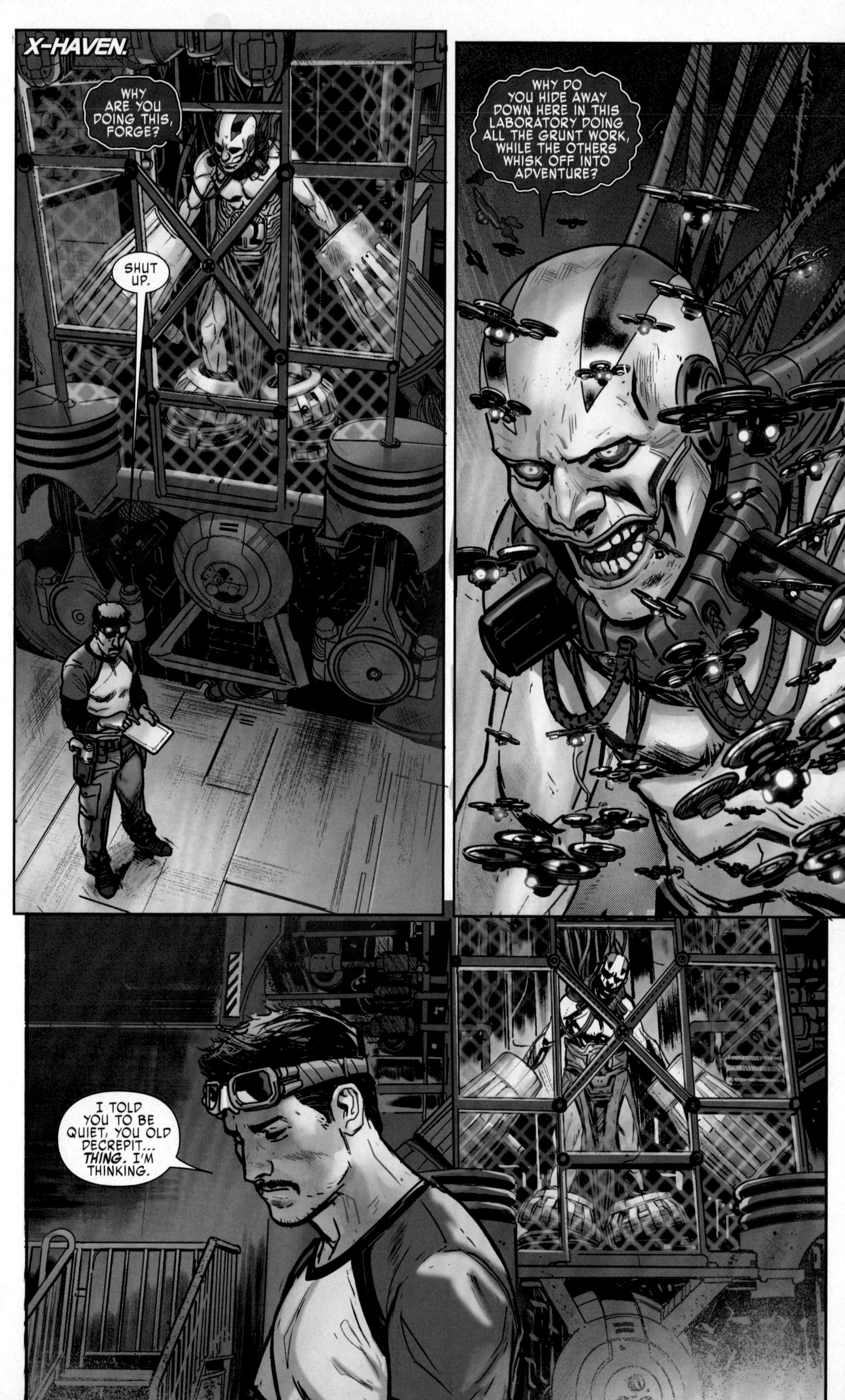
X-HAVEN.
WHY ARE YOU DOING THIS, FORGE?
SHUT UP.
WHY DO YOU HIDE AWAY DOWN HERE IN THIS LABORATORY DOING ALL THE GRUNT WORK, WHILE THE OTHERS WHISK OFF INTO ADVENTURE?
I TOLD YOU TO BE QUIET, YOU OLD DECREPIT... *THING*. I'M THINKING.

HA! AND THAT HAS ALWAYS BEEN YOUR CURSE, HASN'T IT? LOST IN YOUR OWN HEAD WHILE THE WORLD SPINS ON AROUND YOU.
CEREBRA, THE DIAGNOSTICS ON APOCALYPSE ARE COMPLETE. HAVE ALL THE DRONES RETURN TO THEIR DOCKS AND UPLOAD THEIR READINGS.
YES, FORGE.
THEY DON'T RESPECT YOU, BUT YOU KNEW THAT ALREADY. THEY USE YOU. YOU ARE NOTHING MORE THAN THEIR ROBOT, FORGE.
YOU CAN BE SO MUCH MORE THAN THEM. THAT MIND OF YOURS IS A GREATER POWER THAN ANY OF THEIRS. YET THEY KEEP YOU DOWN HERE DOING THEIR DIRTY WORK.
JOIN ME. I WILL MAKE YOU A KING...A GOD. THERE IS NO PROBLEM YOU AND I CANNOT SOLVE TOGETHER... NOT EVEN ORORO MUNROE.

CEREBRA, OPEN THE CELL PLEASE.
ARE YOU CERTAIN, FORGE?
I'M SURE.
THAT'S IT. IT WILL BE SO EASY...
JUST FREE ME AND I WILL FREE YOU.
ZZZIP
I ALREADY ASKED YOU TO BE QUIET. I DON'T LIKE HAVING TO ASK TWICE.

EGYPT.
STOP!
BAMF
YOU ARE RIGHT. I *DO* HAVE FAITH. AND I WILL *NOT* ABANDON YOU!
I KNOW YOU ARE STILL IN THERE, PIOTR. I KNOW THE *REAL YOU* CAN HEAR ME.
THEN, AS ALWAYS, YOU WILL BE DISAPPOINTED!
BAMF
AH!
YOU NEED TO FIGHT THIS, PIOTR! APOCALYPSE IS OLD AND INFIRMED. AKKABA IS NOTHING. *FIGHT IT!*
NO!

BAMF
LET US HELP YOU! FORGE IS WORKING ON A WAY TO UNDO YOUR TRANS-FORMATION.
COME HOME WITH US! COME BACK TO X-HAVEN!
THWAK
UNGH!
X-HAVEN IS DOOMED... JUST LIKE YOU!
I THINK ALL THAT BAMFING JUST MADE HIM MADDER, KURT.
I BELIEVE YOU ARE CORRECT. PERHAPS IT IS TIME FOR PLAN B?

HERE COMES THE CAVALRY!
REALLY SORRY ABOUT THIS, SIR, BUT WE'RE GONNA HAVE TO KICK YOUR BUTT NOW.

X-HAVEN.

I ALMOST DIDN'T HEAR YOU COMING. YOU SHOULD'A BEEN A NINJA, JEANNIE.

I *AM* A NINJA. I'M A *MIND NINJA.*
RIGHT.

IT'S ALMOST PRETTY OUT THERE IF YOU FORGET THE FACT THAT IT'S FULL OF DEMONS AND STUFF.
ALMOST.
GOT A BAD FEELING THOUGH. SOMETHING'S COMING. NOT SURE WHAT, BUT IT AIN'T GOOD.
YOU'RE WORRIED ABOUT HER.
WHO?
DON'T GIVE ME THAT. YOU KNOW WHO. RHYMES WITH "FORM."

SHE CAN TAKE CARE OF HERSELF.
YEAH, BUT KNOWING THAT DOESN'T HELP, DOES IT?
DON'T TRY AND MIND NINJA ME, JEANNIE.
IT'S OKAY TO ADMIT THAT YOU HAVE FEELINGS FOR HER, LOGAN. I MEAN WHO WOULDN'T... SHE'S STORM.
AIN'T GONNA HAPPEN.
WHY NOT? I'M PRETTY SURE SHE FEELS THE SAME.
DON'T MATTER, JEANNIE. LAST TIME I LOVED A WOMAN, I WATCHED HER DIE. NO WAY I'M EVER GONNA GO THROUGH THAT AGAIN.
LOGAN--
GET SOME SLEEP, JEANNIE. GOT A FEELING WE'RE GONNA NEED IT.

IS THIS IT? IS SAPNA HERE?
I THINK SO. HER TRAIL...THE AMBIENT MAGICAL ENERGY SHE LEAVES BEHIND, IT'S VERY FRESH HERE.
THE SIZE OF THESE BONES! WHAT SORT OF CREATURES LIVED HERE?!
BIG ONES. ALL THESE WORLDS... THOSE MYSTICS WE ENCOUNTERED CALLED IT THE LATTICE. DID THAT MEAN ANYTHING TO YOU, ILLYANA?
NO. I HAVE NEVER HEARD OF IT OR THIS WORLD EATER BEFORE. THE FACT THAT SAPNA COULD FIND ALL OF THIS SO SOON AFTER DEVELOPING HER POWERS...WELL, IT'S INCREDIBLE.
WHAT IS IT? IS SHE IN HERE?
I--I'M NOT SURE. SOMETHING IS.

THE FIRE IS FRESH.
CAREFUL, ILLYANA. IT COULD BE A TRAP.
YOU THINK I DON'T KNOW THAT, STORM?
NO NEED FOR THE ATTITUDE, ILLYANA!
I--YOU'RE RIGHT. I'M SORRY, ORORO. I'VE BEEN SHORT WITH YOU LATELY. IT'S JUST, PIOTR AND NOW SAPNA...
I KNOW. I UNDERSTAND. TRUST ME.
KRKT!
SOMEONE IS HERE!

ILLYANA, YOU CAME!
SAPNA!
I WAS SO WORRIED ABOUT YOU.
I--I GOT LOST. SO I HID HERE.
I WAS ALL ALONE IN THE DARK, ILLYANA.
I'M SO SORRY.
IT'S OKAY. HE CAME AND KEPT ME COMPANY.
NOW I'M NOT SCARED ANYMORE.
WHAT DO YOU--

I'M SO GLAD YOU CAME, ILLYANA. JUST LIKE HE SAID YOU WOULD.
ARRGH!
SHRACK!
UNGH!
WE DON'T NEED YOU, THOUGH.
WE DO NEED THIS, HOWEVER.

I'M SORRY, ILLYANA, BUT YOU WOULD STAND IN THE WAY OF WHAT WE HAVE TO DO NEXT. BUT I'LL SAY HI TO EVERYONE IN LIMBO FOR YOU.
YOU SEE, YOU'RE GOING TO HAVE TO STAY *HERE,* ILLYANA...
...FOREVER.

15

STORM?
YOU ARE ALONE, ILLYANA. YOU ARE ALL ALONE.
SAPNA?!
FWOOOSH!
ALL ALONE, JUST LIKE YOU LEFT ME!
AARRRGHHHH!

NO!
ILLYANA?
SAPNA...
SHE ATTACKED US AND LEFT THROUGH A PORTAL. I'VE BEEN TRYING TO WAKE YOU FOR THE LAST TWENTY MINUTES. I WAS GETTING WORRIED.
THIS IS MY FAULT, ORORO. I SHOULD NEVER HAVE LEFT SAPNA ALONE AT X-HAVEN. I SHOULD NOT HAVE BEEN SO AGGRESSIVE WITH HER TRAINING.
I SHOULD HAVE BEEN MORE CAREFUL. AND NOW THAT THING HAS HER.
SHHH. IT'S NOT YOUR FAULT, ILLYANA. YOU COULD NOT HAVE KNOWN. YOU DID EVERYTHING YOU COULD TO HELP THE GIRL.
IT WASN'T ENOUGH, STORM.
WELL, THEN THERE IS ONLY ONE THING WE CAN DO. WE NEED TO FREE HER FROM WHATEVER THAT CREATURE IS THAT IS CONTROLLING HER. SO WHAT SAY WE GET THE HELL OUT OF THIS PLACE?
YES. YOU'RE RIGHT. NO MORE TIME FOR FEELING SORRY FOR MYSELF. WE NEED TO FIND HER.
I THINK SAPNA WENT BACK TO LIMBO, STORM.
WHY DO YOU SAY THAT?
SHE TOOK THE SOULSWORD. I THINK THAT THING HAD HER LURE US HERE JUST SO THEY COULD GET IT. TO CONTROL THE SWORD IS TO CONTROL LIMBO.

BUT GETTING BACK IS GOING TO BE EASIER SAID THAN DONE. THE PORTAL THAT SAPNA AND THAT THING USED TO GET BACK TO LIMBO IS GONE. SHE SEALED IT BEHIND HER.
BUT THE DOORWAY WE CAME THROUGH TO GET TO THIS REALM IS STILL HERE.
SO IT SEEMS WE ONLY HAVE ONE OPTION, TO RETRACE OUR STEPS.
THOSE MYSTICS WHO ATTACKED US EARLIER, THEY WERE ENEMIES OF WHATEVER HAS CONTROL OF SAPNA. THEY SEEMED TO HAVE ANSWERS TO WHAT THAT THING IS. THEY CALLED IT THE WORLD EATER. WE MAY NEED TO CONVINCE THEM TO HELP US.
IF THEY DON'T KILL US FIRST.
X-HAVEN MAY BE AT RISK. WE NEED TO HURRY.
STORM, ONE MORE THING...
YES?
TELL ANYONE I CRIED, AND I WILL DISMEMBER YOU.
THAT'S MY GIRL.

EGYPT.
--I'M REALLY SORRY, SIR.
THOOM!
NICE SHOT, GLOBBER!
WE NEED *HELP!* WE CAN'T HOLD HIM MUCH LONGER!
DO NOT WORRY, NIGHTCRAWLER--

SHRACK!
--I HAVE HIM!
ABOUT TIME YOU GUYS SHOWED UP. I WAS STARTING TO WORRY.
EXCELLENT WORK.
I AM SORRY, PIOTR. BUT THIS IS FOR YOUR OWN GOOD.
GOOD WORK, KURT, AND GOOD TIMING. I FINISHED CEREBRA'S REPAIRS JUST IN TIME, I SEE.
SPEAKING OF WHICH, CEREBRA, GO GRAB BOBBY AND THE KIDS FROM EGYPT.
YES. I WOULD HATE TO SEE WHAT TROUBLE THE CHILDREN WOULD GET UP TO WITHOUT ME.
SHRACK!
YOU CANNOT HOLD ME!
THOOM!

IT IS I. THERE IS NO NEED TO TROUBLE YOURSELF. WE ARE EXACTLY WHERE WE NEED TO BE.
QUIET!
EASY, FORGE. APOCALYPSE IS JUST TRYING TO DISTRACT YOU. HE KNOWS YOU ARE THE ONLY ONE WHO CAN HELP PIOTR.
THAT'S JUST IT, KURT...I DON'T KNOW IF I CAN.
I HAVE NEVER SEEN A PROBLEM YOU COULD NOT SOLVE, FORGE. DO NOT LET THAT MONSTER GET INTO YOUR HEAD.
YOU KNOW ALL ABOUT MONSTERS IN YOUR HEAD, DON'T YOU, NIGHTCRAWLER?
YOU HAVE ALREADY LOST, APOCALYPSE.
HAVE I?
YOU NEED ME. FORGE WILL FAIL AND HE KNOWS IT. I AM THE ONLY ONE WHO CAN SAVE YOUR BELOVED PIOTR. IT IS ONLY A MATTER OF TIME UNTIL YOU START BEGGING.

THIS WAY, HURRY!
ARE YOU SURE THIS IS THE RIGHT WAY, ILLYANA?
WE'VE BEEN THROUGH THIS WORLD BEFORE. I THINK WE'RE GOING IN CIRCLES!
I'M SURE! TRUST ME, STORM!
HERE! I TOLD YOU!
THANK THE GODDESS. I WAS WORRIED WE WOULD NEVER FIND IT!
ILLYANA!
I SEE HIM.
TH- THEY'RE BACK!

THEY'RE BACK! THEY'RE BACK!
QUIET, OLD MAN, OR I'LL BURN THE TONGUE FROM YOUR MOUTH!
WHAT THE BLAZES ARE YOU YELLING ABOUT, JACK, I WAS TAKING A LEA--WHOA!
THE WITCHES!
LET HIM GO!
I DON'T THINK SO. YOU ALL NEED TO STAND DOWN!
LISTEN, ALL OF YOU. WE DID NOT COME HERE TO FIGHT! I DO NOT KNOW WHO YOU THINK WE ARE, BUT I HAVE A FEELING WE ARE ALL FACING THE SAME ENEMY. THIS "WORLD EATER."
HOW THE HELL WE SUPPOSED TO TRUST THE LIKES OF YOU?!
PLEASE. WE HAVE NO IDEA WHERE WE ARE. WE HAVE NO IDEA HOW TO GET HOME. ALL WE KNOW IS THAT THING HAS OUR FRIEND...SHE'S JUST A CHILD. ALL I WANT TO DO IS HELP HER.
SPECTRA...
HEY!
I CAN DETERMINE IF YOU ARE TELLING THE TRUTH. BUT YOU MUST PERMIT ME. IF YOU HAVE NOTHING TO HIDE...

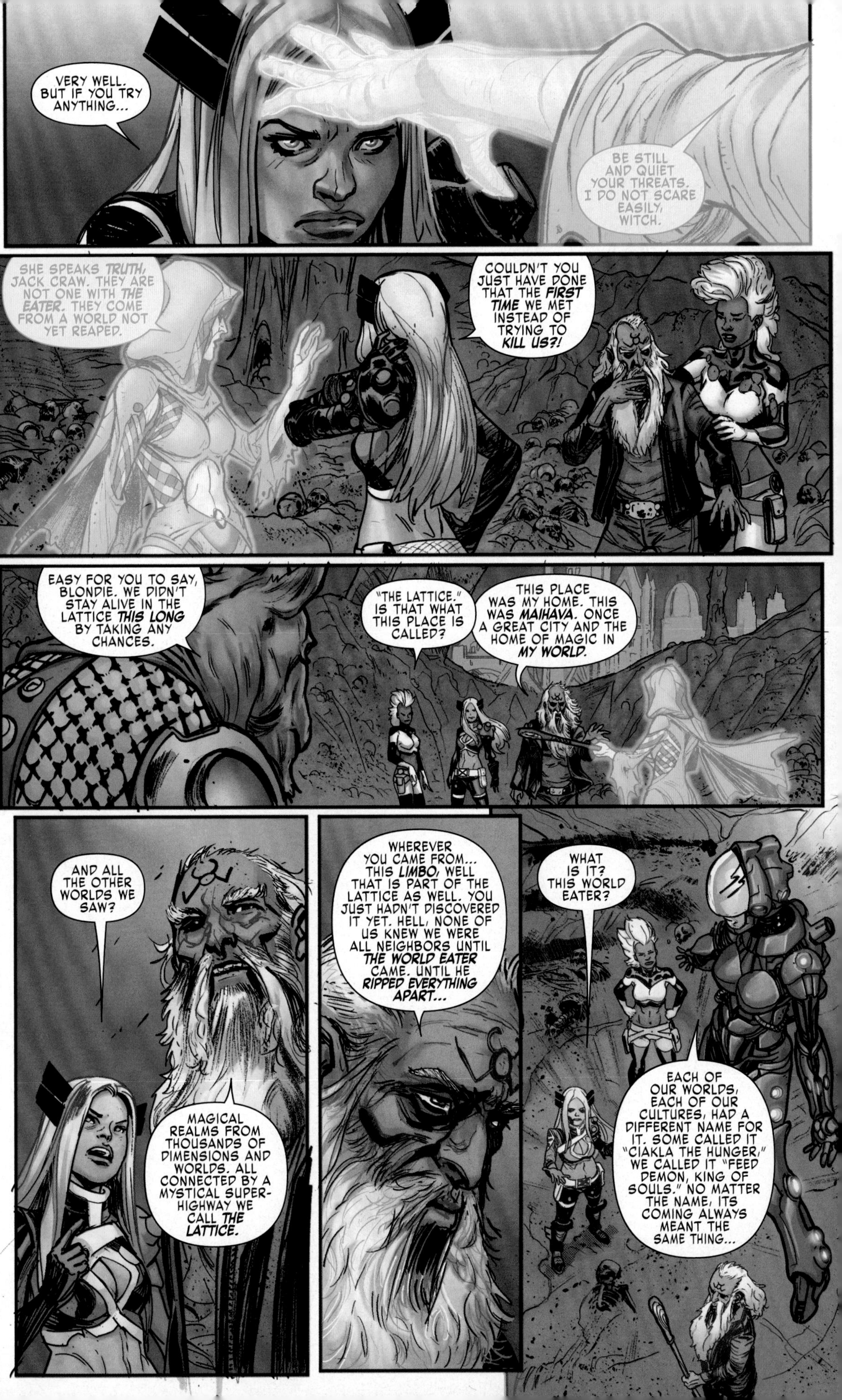

VERY WELL. BUT IF YOU TRY ANYTHING...
BE STILL AND QUIET YOUR THREATS. I DO NOT SCARE EASILY, WITCH.

SHE SPEAKS *TRUTH*, JACK CRAW. THEY ARE NOT ONE WITH *THE EATER*. THEY COME FROM A WORLD NOT YET REAPED.
COULDN'T YOU JUST HAVE DONE THAT THE ***FIRST TIME*** WE MET INSTEAD OF TRYING TO ***KILL US?!***

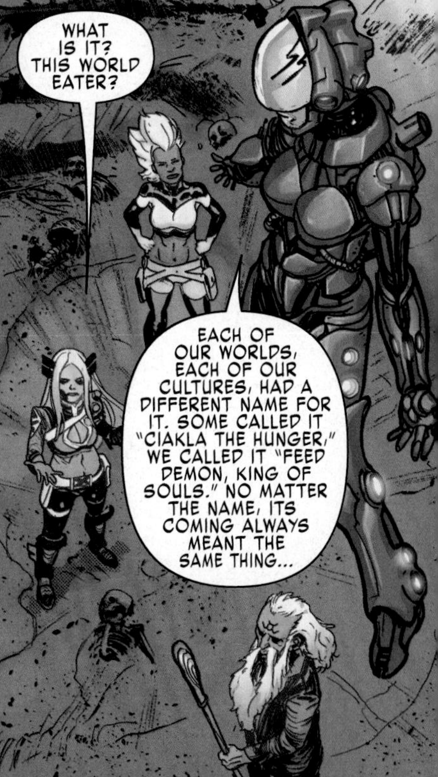

"...THE END OF EVERYTHING.
"IT LIVES ONLY TO CONSUME. IT FEEDS OFF PLACES WHERE GREAT MAGIC LIVES.

"IT IS ANTI-MAGIC. IT IS ANTI-LIFE. ONE BY ONE IT HAS EATEN ITS WAY THROUGH THE LATTICE, DEVOURING ALL OF OUR WORLDS AND ***THOUSANDS OF OTHERS.*** LEAVING ONLY HUSKS IN ITS WAKE.
"THE GREAT IRONY IS THAT THE WORLD EATER IS NEARL ***POWERLESS*** ON HIS OWN. T MOVE THROUGH THE LATTICE IT REQUIRES A ***HOST*** FROM EACH WORLD.
"IT TOOK A VESSEL FROM EACH WORLD IT CONSUMED. WITHOUT THEM IT CANNOT FEED AND IT CANNOT TRAVEL THE LATTICE."

AND WHO ARE YOU, THEN? SURVIVORS?
INDEED. THE LAST MYSTICS LEFT ALIVE FROM EACH OF OUR WORLDS. OUR POWER SAVED US, BUT NOT OUR HOMES. SO NOW WE DO WHAT WE CAN, TRYING TO FIND A WEAKNESS...TRYING TO FIND A WAY TO STOP IT. BUT SO FAR...
I FEAR THAT THIS CHILD YOU SEEK IS ALREADY LOST. THE WORLD EATER IS USING HER AS ITS HOST NOW. TOGETHER, THEY WILL CONSUME YOUR WORLD, JUST LIKE ALL OF OURS.
THESE HOSTS, WHAT HAPPENED TO THE OTHERS? THE ONES IT USED TO CONSUME ALL THESE WORLDS?
WHEN IT IS DONE FEEDING, IT MOVES ON. IT TAKES A NEW HOST FROM A NEW WORLD.
WHAT ARE YOU SAYING?! SPIT IT OUT, OLD WIZARD!
I'M SAYING THERE IS NO HOPE FOR YOUR FRIEND. THIS THING CONSUMES EVERYTHING. ALL ITS PAST HOSTS ARE DEAD.
NO!
SHRACK!

THERE MUST BE A WAY BACK!
ILLYANA...
NO, ORORO. I CAN STILL FEEL LIMBO, OUR WORLD, JUST BEYOND THE VEIL OF THIS ONE. I HAVE TO KEEP SPELL-CASTING. I HAVE TO TRY!
YOUR CONNECTION TO YOUR WORLD IS THE KEY. HMM...
WHAT IS IT, JACK?
WE'RE ALL MYSTICS. WE ALL HAVE POWER. MAYBE IF WE CHANNEL IT THROUGH THE GIRL...WITH HER CONNECTION TO HER WORLD, SHE MIGHT BE ABLE TO BREAK THROUGH.
EVEN IF THE GIRL CAN SURVIVE ALL OF OUR POWER, THEN WHAT? WE FACE THE WORLD EATER HEAD-ON, JACK? IT'S SUICIDE!
IT'S TOO DANGEROUS, ILLYANA.
I DON'T CARE. IT'S NOT JUST SAPNA, STORM. X-HAVEN WILL FALL IF WE DON'T STOP THIS THING.
I'M READY. DO IT!

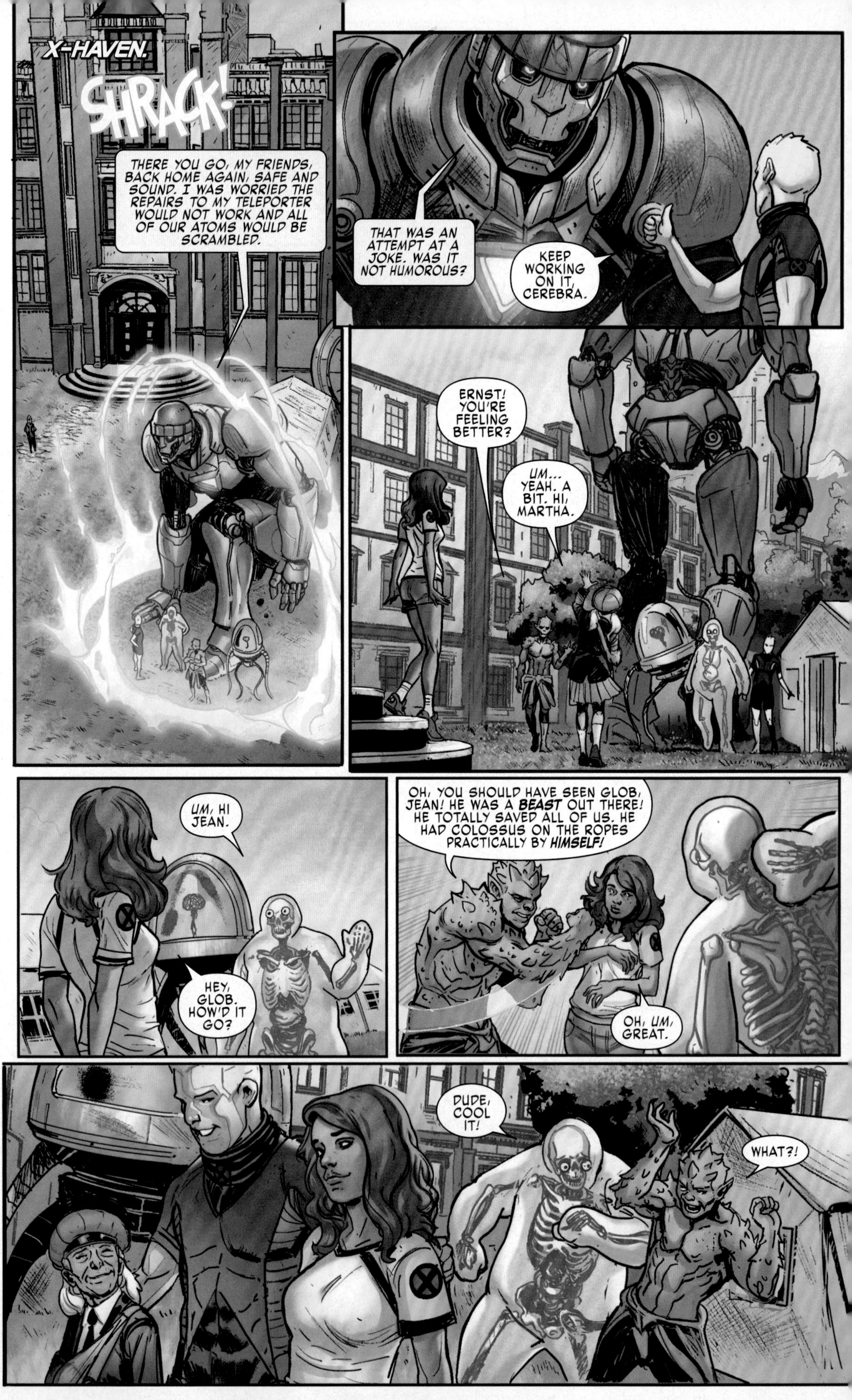

X-HAVEN.

SHRACK!

THERE YOU GO, MY FRIENDS, BACK HOME AGAIN, SAFE AND SOUND. I WAS WORRIED THE REPAIRS TO MY TELEPORTER WOULD NOT WORK AND ALL OF OUR ATOMS WOULD BE SCRAMBLED.

THAT WAS AN ATTEMPT AT A JOKE. WAS IT NOT HUMOROUS?

KEEP WORKING ON IT, CEREBRA.

ERNST! YOU'RE FEELING BETTER?

UM... YEAH. A BIT. HI, MARTHA.

ACTUALLY, UM, JEAN, THERE WAS SOMETHING I WAS WANTING TO TALK TO YOU ABOUT.
SURE, GLOB. WHAT'S UP?
WELL, UH, I KNOW THERE'S NOT A LOT OF FREE TIME AROUND HERE LATELY. YOU KNOW, WITH BEING SENT TO THE FUTURE TO FIGHT APOCALYPSE, AND THE WHOLE TERRIGEN MIST THING, BUT, UM...
...I WAS WONDERING IF YOU WANTED TO--I MEAN MAYBE SOMETIME WE COULD--
OH, NEVER MIND, I DIDN'T MEAN TO UPSET YOU OR ANYTHING.
WHAT? NO...IT'S NOT YOU, GLOB.
THERE'S SOMETHING OUT THERE. A--A PRESENCE. AND IT'S--
NO!
JEAN?!
JEAN!

I'M NO CLOSER TO FIGURING OUT COLOSSUS' TRANS-FORMATION, LET ALONE HOW TO REVERSE IT. ALL OF THE TESTS I TOOK ON APOCALYPSE ARE DEAD ENDS.
WELL, KEEP POKING AROUND, THEN! WE GOTTA GET PETE BACK TO NORMAL.
YOU DON'T THINK I KNOW THAT, LOGAN?! I'M DOING EVERYTHING I CAN!
THE SOLUTION IS SO SIMPLE. IT IS RIGHT BEFORE YOUR EYES, FORGE. I WILL CHANGE COLOSSUS BACK TO HIS OLD SELF.
ALL YOU HAVE TO DO IS SET ME FREE.
YOU'LL NEVER BE FREE. YOU'LL ROT DOWN HERE BEFORE WE--
CHOOM!
THE HELL WAS THAT?!
AH, #&%$.
MY GOD...

"...IT'S SAPNA!"

JEAN, PLEASE! SOMEBODY HELP!
ARE YOU SURE, ILLYANA?
I'M SURE. IT'S TIME, BEFORE MY CONNECTION TO LIMBO FADES COMPLETELY. ALL OF YOU, GIVE ME YOUR POWER! EVERYTHING YOU HAVE...
"...DON'T HOLD BACK!"
SNIKT!
YOU READY, ICEPICK?
DIDN'T WE ALREADY DO THIS DEMON-FIGHTING THING ONCE BEFORE?
WE ARE ALL THAT STANDS BETWEEN THESE BEASTS AND X-HAVEN. WE MUST HOLD THE LINE!

DO YOU HEAR THAT? THE END IS HERE. LET ME GIVE YOU COLOSSUS BACK. RELEASE ME.
SHRACK!
ARRRRGHH!
STOP!
"YOU'RE KILLING HER!"
SHE WILL CONSUME EVERYTHING! SHE WILL CONSUME EVERYTHING!
THE SOUL-SWORD IS MINE. LIMBO IS MINE. GO AHEAD AND SCURRY LIKE ANTS. IT MAKES NO DIFFERENCE. THIS IS THE END.

AND IN THE END IT ALL FALLS.

ANNUAL #1 VARIANT BY SKOTTIE YOUNG

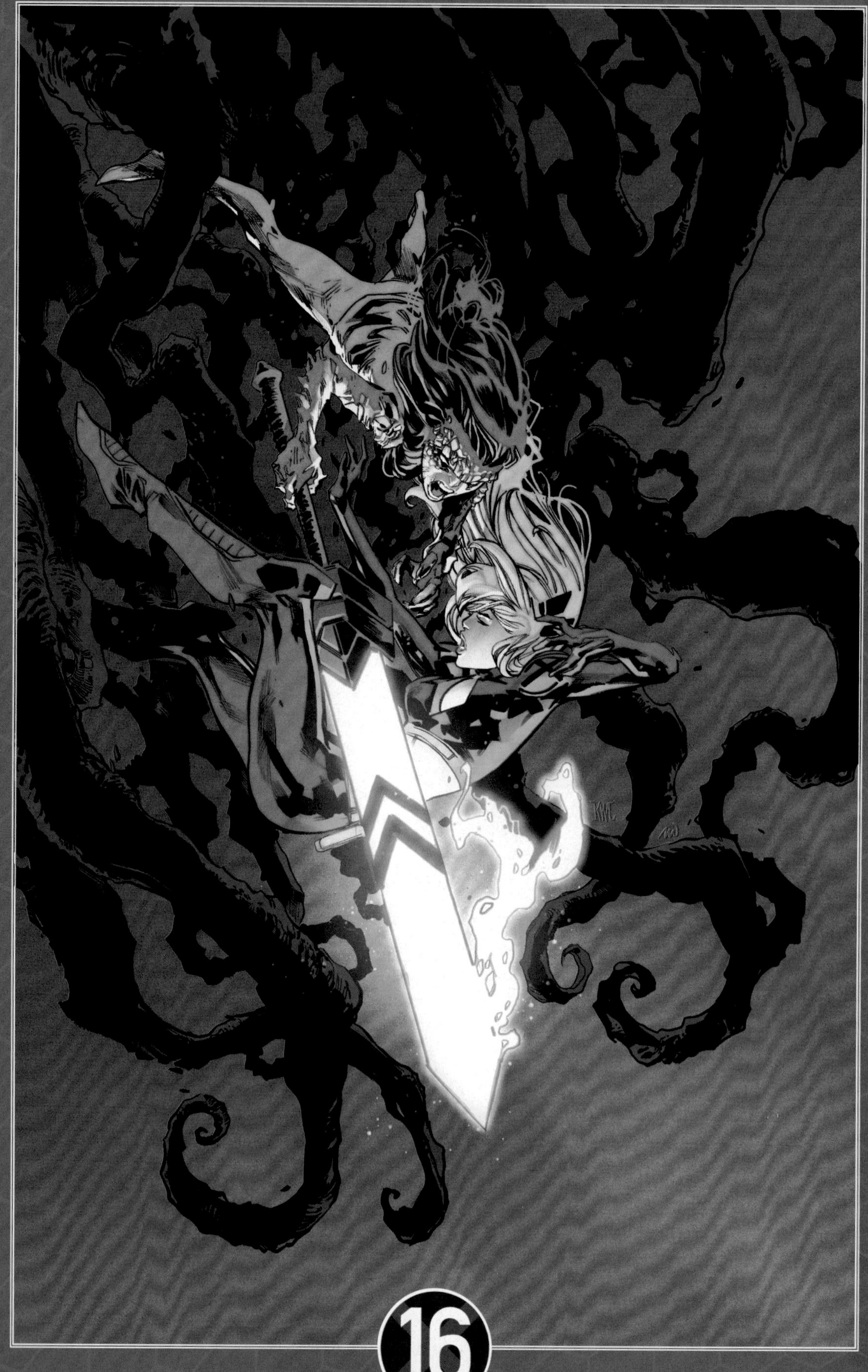
16

LIMBO.
LOGAN, WE NEED HELP!
WHATEVER THAT THING IS THAT HAS SAPNA HAS MADE HER WAY TOO POWERFUL.
AIN'T NO HELP COMING, BOBBY. WE'RE IT.
YOU CAN'T FIGHT HER ALONE!
SNIKT
WATCH ME.

ARRRGHH!
SILLY ANIMAL.
LOGAN!
THOOOM

I HAVE TO GET OUT THERE.
GO, KURT. THERE'S NOTHING YOU CAN DO HERE TO HELP PETE.
YES, LEAVE FORGE IN THE BOWELS OF THIS CRYPT LIKE YOU ALWAYS DO.

SHUT UP, APOCALYPSE, OR I SWEAR TO GOD I'LL *STITCH* YOUR MOUTH SHUT THIS TIME!

AND THEN I WILL BREAK YOU, LITTLE MAN!

HELP! I NEED HELP!
JEAN?!

IT--YOU CAN'T STOP IT! ITS MIND IS MASSIVE... ENDLESS AND COLD! AND IT HAS HER NOW. IT HAS SAPNA. ***SHE'S GOING TO KILL US ALL!***

ARRRRGHH!
STOP! YOU'RE KILLING HER!
NO... I--
TH-THERE. I CAN--I CAN ALMOST BREAK THROUGH, BUT--TAKING ALL MY FOCUS JUST TO FIND LIMBO--
GIVE IT TO ME, ILLYANA!
WHAT?

GIVE ME THE POWER! ALL OF IT!
LET ME BE YOUR LIGHTNING ROD!

JEAN, CALM DOWN!
NO HOPE! ONLY DARKNESS!
THIS IS THE END! YOU NEED ALL THE HELP YOU CAN GET. SET ME FREE AND I WILL GIVE YOU COLOSSUS BACK!
KZZTZ

RMMMBBBLLLL
FEED! CONSUME IT ALL! THERE IS NOTHING LEFT TO STOP US!
THUNDER?

KA-KOOOM
WHA--?
GET THE HELL AWAY FROM MY SCHOOL.

I HAVE YOU.
THE REST OF YOU, YOU NEED TO PROTECT THE SCHOOL FROM THOSE DEMONS!
WHAT? AND LEAVE YOU ALONE AGAINST HER?!
THIS IS MY DOMAIN.
I'M THE ONLY ONE WHO CAN STOP HER.

YOU THINK YOU CAN STOP ME, WHEN SO MANY OTHERS HAVE FAILED? THOUSANDS OF WITCHES AND SORCERERS. THOUSANDS OF SO-CALLED HEROES AND CHAMPIONS. ALL DEAD, JUST LIKE THEIR WORLDS.
NO. BECAUSE IT'S NOT YOU I WANT, WORLD EATER. I'VE COME FOR SAPNA.
I KNOW YOU CAN HEAR ME, SAPNA! DO NOT BE AFRAID!
UNGH!
ILLYANA-- PLEASE--I DON'T WANT TO DO THIS!
I KNOW, GIRL, I KNOW! TAKE MY HAND! IGNORE THAT THING. COME BACK TO ME!

YOU ARE A SENTIMENTAL FOOL.
FWOOSH
I KNOW EVERY THOUGHT IN HER YOUNG HEAD. SHE HATES YOU.
DO YOU WANT TO KNOW THE TRUTH? I HAVE HAD MY EYE ON THIS WORLD FOR A LONG TIME. IT WAS YOU I HAD CHOSEN TO BE MY HOST, ILLYANA RASPUTIN. TO CONTROL YOU WAS TO CONTROL LIMBO.
BUT THEN YOU TOOK IN THE GIRL. AND SHE WAS SO WEAK, SO VULNERABLE.
YOU OPENED HER EYES TO MAGIC. AFTER THAT, IT WAS SO EASY TO CALL TO HER. TO LURE HER AWAY! TO CONSUME HER SOUL!
ARRRGHH!

I WILL NEVER CHANGE COLOSSUS BACK! NEVER! NOT UNLESS YOU SET ME FREE!
FORGE, CAN YOU DO IT? CAN YOU FIX PIOTR?
KURT! YOU'RE NOT SERIOUSLY CONSIDERING--
CAN YOU DO IT OR NOT?
I--
NO. I'VE TRIED EVERYTHING. I CAN'T DO IT, KURT. I JUST--I FAILED.
EITHER WAY, WE CAN'T MAKE A DEAL WITH APOCALYPSE!
PIOTR IS MY BEST FRIEND. I CANNOT LEAVE HIM LIKE THIS! I WILL NOT.
AND IT WOULD NOT BE THE FIRST TIME I SOLD MY SOUL.

SAPNA! STOP! LISTEN TO ME! YOU HAVE TO FIGHT THIS!
X-HAVEN, SAPNA! YOU ARE GOING TO DESTROY X-HAVEN AND EVERYONE IN IT! PLEASE!
LET HER GO!
YOUR WORDS MEAN NOTHING! HER FLESH IS MINE! HER SOUL IS MINE!
ILLYANA! THE SCHOOL!

"IT'S DESTROYING THE SCHOOL!"
DO IT, NIGHTCRAWLER! FREE ME AND COLOSSUS IS YOURS.
KURT, YOU CAN'T!
SAPNA, PLEASE...PLEASE STOP!
FINE. YOU WIN, APOCALYPSE. TRANSFORM PIOTR BACK AND I WILL FREE YOU FROM THIS PLACE.
THIS WORLD WILL DIE, JACK! JUST LIKE ALL THE OTHERS! THE WORLD EATER HAS WON!
X-HAVEN IS ALL WE HAVE... DON'T MAKE ME DO THIS, SAPNA!

DO IT, FORGE.
KURT--
YOU MUST TRUST ME!
NO! I DO NOT WANT THIS! I AM YOURS, MASTER! DO NOT CHANGE ME BACK!
QUIET, MY HORSEMAN. YOU HAVE BEEN LOYAL...
...NOW IT IS TIME TO REST.
ARRRGHHH!

NOW RELEASE ME!
KURT, DON'T!
BAMF
BAMF
I TOLD YOU TO TRUST ME, FORGE. BESIDES...
...WE HAD A DEAL.
WHAT IS THIS?!
BAMF
YOUR FREEDOM.
NO!

SAPNA! IF YOU CAN HEAR ME...
...I'M SO SORRY.
ARRRGH!
KKT!
ILL-ILLYANA?

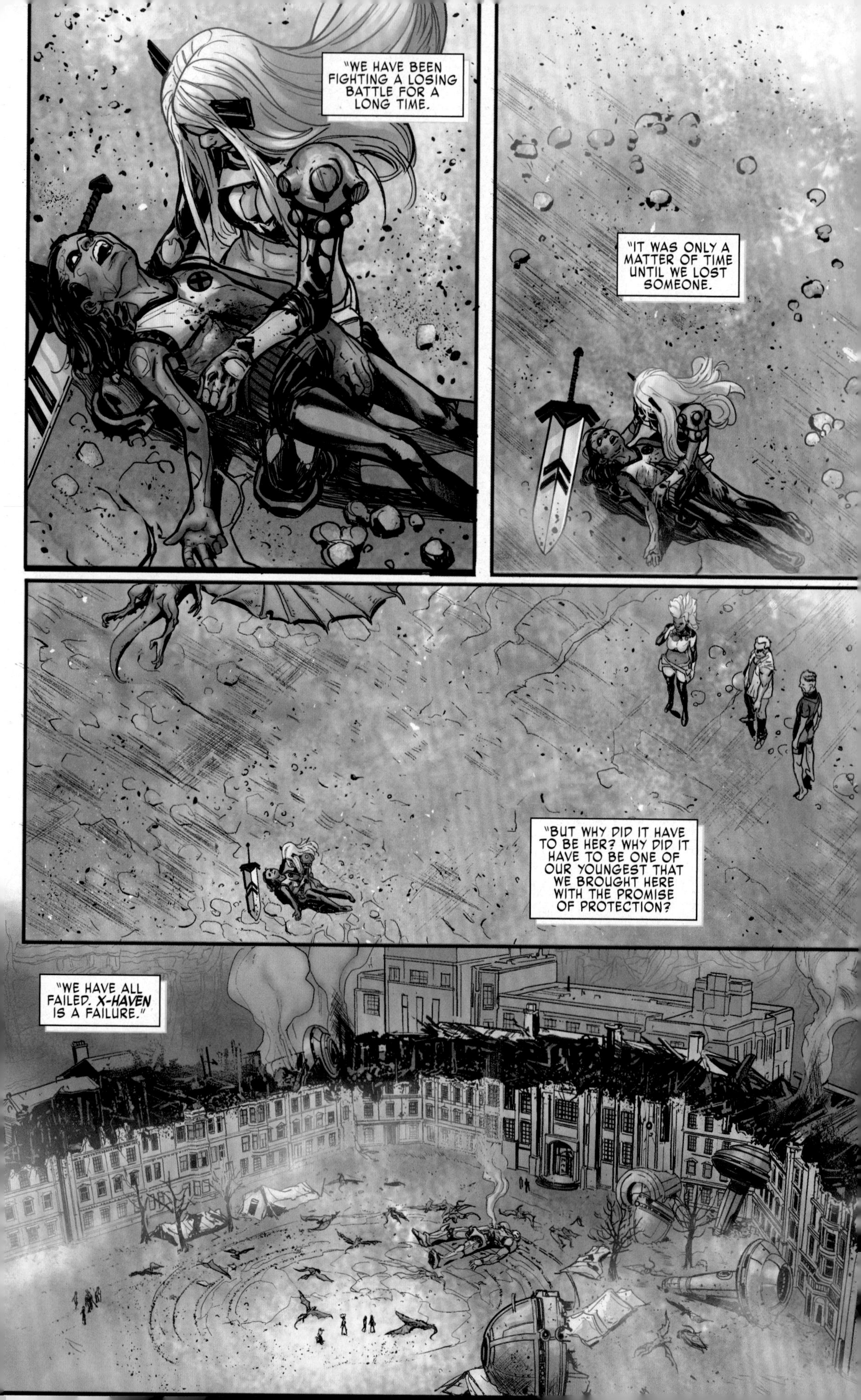

"BUT WHY DID IT HAVE TO BE HER? WHY DID IT HAVE TO BE ONE OF OUR YOUNGEST THAT WE BROUGHT HERE WITH THE PROMISE OF PROTECTION?

"WE HAVE ALL FAILED. *X-HAVEN* IS A FAILURE."

IT'S BEEN THREE DAYS SINCE SAPNA DIED. THREE DAYS SINCE WE ALMOST LOST THE SCHOOL.
WE NEED TO MAKE A CHANGE. WE *CAN'T* GO ON LIKE THIS.

WHAT ARE YOU SAYING, 'RO?
WE CAN'T STAY HERE. NOT AFTER THIS. NOT IF WE EXPECT TO SAFELY HARBOR ANY MORE MUTANTS.
WHAT ABOUT THE TERRIGEN MIST?

WE'VE HIDDEN FOR TOO LONG. IT'S TIME WE FACED THINGS. IT'S TIME WE RECLAIMED OUR PLACE IN THE WORLD *ONE WAY* OR *ANOTHER.*

I FEEL GUILTY SAYING THIS, GIVEN EVERYTHING THAT'S HAPPENED, BUT I ACTUALLY FEEL HAPPIER THAN I HAVE IN A LONG TIME, PIOTR.
I--I DIDN'T REALIZE HOW MUCH I MISSED YOU, MY FRIEND.

I MISSED YOU TOO, MY FRIEND. THANK YOU.
YOU CAME LOOKING FOR ME WHEN I WAS LOST. IT WAS THE LEAST I COULD DO.
I AM WORRIED ABOUT MY SISTER.
ILLYANA IS STRONG, PIOTR...

"...SHE JUST NEEDS TIME."
ILLYANA?
SAPNA?!
THE END?

EXTRAORDINARY X-MEN ANNUAL #1

EXTRAORDINARY X-MEN

A CLOUD OF TERRIGEN MIST HAS BEEN CIRCLING THE GLOBE SINCE BLACK BOLT, THE FORMER INHUMAN LEADER, RELEASED IT FROM THE INHUMAN CITY OF ATTILAN. TRADITIONALLY RESERVED AS PART OF A COMING-OF-AGE CEREMONY, THE TERRIGEN TRIGGERS TRANSFORMATION (AND IN MANY CASES UNLEASHES LATENT POWERS) FOR INHUMANS. AS THE TERRIGEN SPREADS ACROSS THE PLANET, MANY PEOPLE WHO WERE PREVIOUSLY UNAWARE OF INHUMAN DNA IN THEIR GENETIC MAKEUP HAVE BEEN TRANSFORMING AS THEY COME INTO CONTACT WITH THE MIST. CASE IN POINT: NINE-YEAR-OLD LUNELLA LAFAYETTE, WHO'S USING HER GENIUS INTELLECT TO TRY TO REVERSE HER CONDITION.

BUT THERE IS ANOTHER SIDE EFFECT OF THE MIST: IT IS A DEADLY POISON TO ANYONE WITH THE MUTANT X-GENE. TO MAINTAIN A SAFE DISTANCE FROM THE MIST, THE X-MEN HAVE ESTABLISHED A REFUGE CALLED X-HAVEN IN THE DIMENSION OF LIMBO WHERE THE TERRIGEN CANNOT REACH.

BUT THERE ARE STILL OTHER MUTANTS ON EARTH WHO NEED TO MAINTAIN A SAFE DISTANCE FROM THE ROLLING MIST...

STORM'S OFFICE, X-HAVEN.
IF YOU HAVE SOMEWHERE MORE IMPORTANT TO BE, MS. MUNROE, PLEASE DON'T LET US KEEP YOU.

I'M SORRY, I JUST ASSUMED THAT AS WE HAVE--

--ROUGHLY FORTY MINUTES BEFORE THE TERRIGEN MIST ROLLS OVER ONE OF YOUR SUPER-POWERED PRISONS--
--WHERE TWO MUTANTS ARE CURRENTLY BEING HELD WHO WILL LIKELY DIE IF THEY COME INTO CONTACT WITH THE CLOUD--

--IT MIGHT BE A GOOD IDEA TO KEEP AN EYE ON THE TIME.
BUT IF YOU'RE TELLING ME THE BRITISH GOVERNMENT WON'T DO ANYTHING TO HELP, I GUESS IT ISN'T IMPORTANT.

THE BRITISH GOVERNMENT HASN'T OFFICIALLY RECOGNIZED THE TERRIGEN MIST AS HARMFUL TO MUTANTS.

IF WE MOVED THESE PRISONERS IT WOULD SET A DANGEROUS PRECEDENT AND RIGHT NOW THE POLITICS OF THAT ARE AWFULLY TRICKY--
SO YOU'LL LET THEM DIE RATHER THAN BE POLITICALLY INCONVENIENCED?

WHY ARE WE EVEN ARGUING THIS? THEY'RE PRISONERS, FOR GOD'S SAKE.
THEY MADE THEIR DECISION. THEY CAN TAKE THE CONSEQUENCES.
RAMROD AND RUCKUS WERE EACH SENTENCED TO THIRTEEN YEARS IN PRISON.
NOT DEATH.

I'M SORRY, BUT THERE'S NOTHING WE CAN DO.

I DON'T KNOW ABOUT THAT.
JEAN? I'VE HIT A BRICK WALL. LOOKS LIKE IT'S UP TO YOU NOW.

THE WORKSHOP, X-HAVEN.
OKAY, STORM, WE'LL MOVE ON TO PLAN B.
THEN WE NEED TO GET MOVING. I WISH WE HAD MORE PREP TIME...

WHERE'S LOGAN?

LOGAN?

THIS BETTER BE GOOD, JEANNIE. I'M TYING ONE ON HERE.

WE NEED YOU TO BREAK INTO A PRISON.
WELL, OKAY, THAT'S PRETTY GOOD.

I'VE CHANGED MY MIND. THIS IS A BAD IDEA.
WELL, WE DON'T HAVE ANY OTHER OPTIONS, SO DEAL WITH IT.
STORM'S GETTING NOWHERE WITH THE DIPLOMATIC ROUTE, SO WE NEED TO TAKE MATTERS INTO OUR OWN HANDS IF WE'RE GOING TO SAVE THESE MUTANTS.
HERE'S WHAT WE'RE UP AGAINST.
WE ESTIMATE THAT THE TERRIGEN CLOUD WILL REACH THE PRISON IN LESS THAN FORTY MINUTES.
THERE ARE CAMERAS EVERYWHERE AND THE NULLIFIERS MAKE THE PRISON A *POWERS-FREE ZONE*--BUT ONLY *INSIDE* THE PRISON WALLS.

SO, HOW DO WE DO THIS? NIGHTCRAWLER CAN TELEPORT IN, BUT THEN WHAT?
THE CAMERAS I CAN LOOP. BUT THE NULLIFIERS HAVE TIGHT SAFEGUARDS.
THEY'LL KNOW IF I'M TAMPERING WITH THEM AND SHUT EVERYTHING DOWN.
WHAT IF YOU JUST SHUT THEM DOWN FOR FIVE SECONDS, FORGE? ENOUGH TIME TO GET OUT BUT SHORT ENOUGH TO LOOK LIKE A BLIP?
YEAH, I DOUBT THEY WOULD NOTICE THAT.
SO, WE CUT THE NULLIFIER AT EXACTLY TEN MINUTES PAST THREE X-HAVEN TIME. THAT SHOULD GIVE US ENOUGH TIME TO FIND THEM BEFORE THE CLOUD HITS.
NIGHTCRAWLER JUST NEEDS TO TELEPORT OUT IN THAT FIVE-SECOND WINDOW.
BUT EVEN IF WE TAKE OUT THE CAMERAS, THE GUARDS AND PRISONERS WILL TRY TO STOP US.
NOT IF THEY DON'T SEE YOU.
THE BRITISH HAVE SOME OF THE BEST ANTI-POWERS TECH IN THE WORLD.
BUT I THINK THAT IF I PUSH AS HARD AS I CAN FROM OUTSIDE, I SHOULD BE ABLE TO PSYCHICALLY CLOAK YOU.

YOU'LL HAVE TO PUSH PRETTY HARD, JEAN. IT WILL TAKE ALL OF YOUR CONCENTRATION. ILLYANA SHOULD STAY OUTSIDE AND KEEP AN EYE ON YOU.
AND NIGHTCRAWLER'S GOING TO NEED BACKUP INSIDE AS WELL.

CAN'T YOU SEND ICEBOY?
DON'T TELL ME YOU'RE GETTING SCARED IN YOUR OLD AGE, LOGAN.
NOT SCARED, JUST LAZY.

THIS IS WHO YOU'RE RESCUING. RUCKUS AND RAMROD. EX-NASTY BOYS AND ALL-ROUND BAD GUYS CURRENTLY SERVING TIME FOR ATTEMPTED BANK ROBBERY.
I RECOGNIZE THESE TWO. ARE THEY REALLY WORTH RISKING AN *INTERNATIONAL INCIDENT* OVER IF WE GET CAUGHT?

HAVE YOU GOT A BETTER PLAN, LOGAN?
YEAH, LET THE CLOUD ROLL OVER THE PRISON AND GET ON WITH OUR DAY.
I SAID A **BETTER** PLAN.

BUT LOGAN'S RIGHT.
IF WE GET CAUGHT BREAKING INTO A BRITISH PRISON, THEY'LL COME AFTER US HARD.

SO LET'S NOT GET CAUGHT.

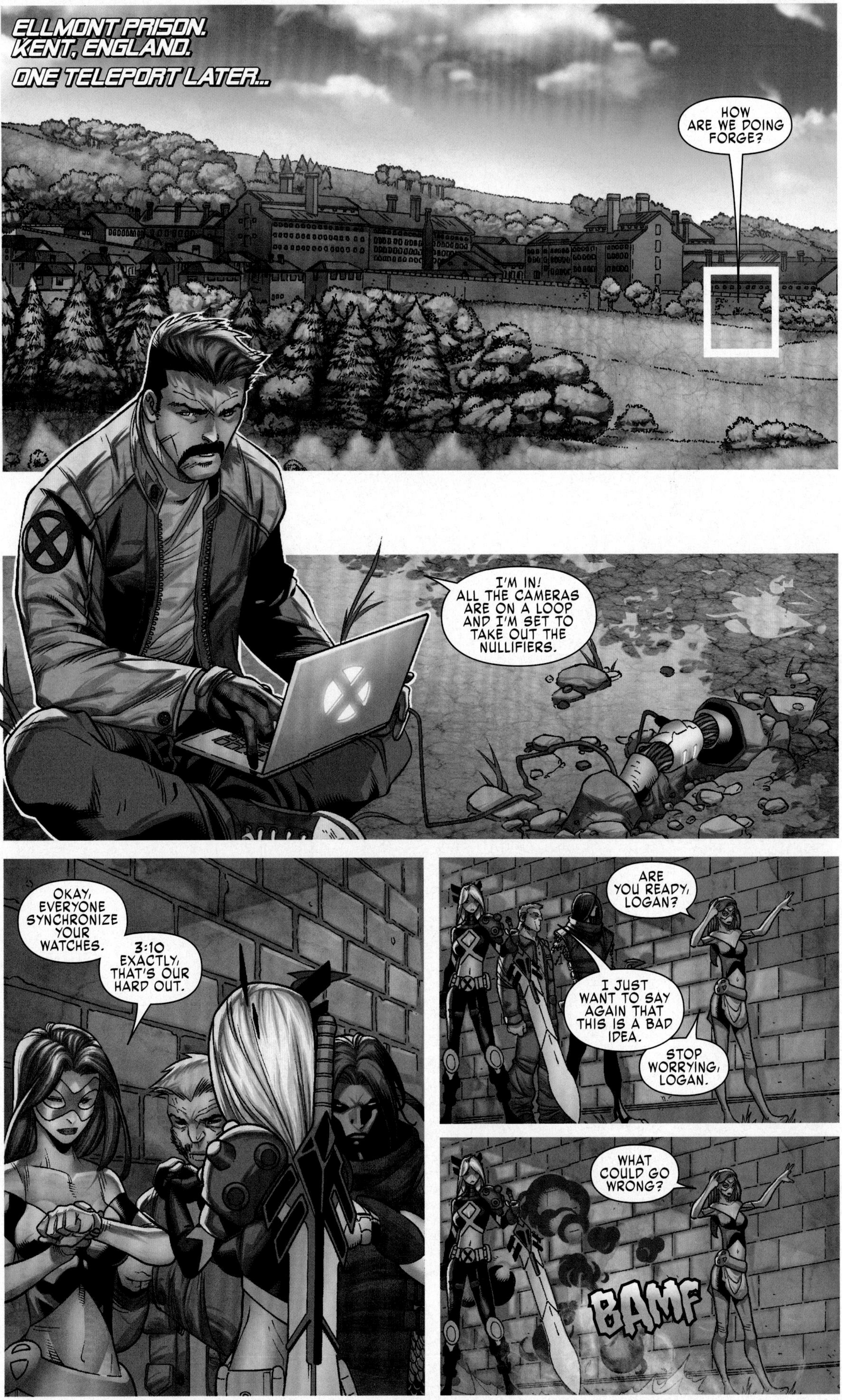

ELLMONT PRISON.
KENT, ENGLAND.
ONE TELEPORT LATER...

HOW ARE WE DOING FORGE?

I'M IN! ALL THE CAMERAS ARE ON A LOOP AND I'M SET TO TAKE OUT THE NULLIFIERS.

OKAY, LET'S--
AH, CRAP.
HOW ARE WE MEANT TO SNEAK THROUGH THIS? THEY'LL TEAR US APART.
JUST KEEP GOING! THEY CAN'T SEE US-- WE SHOULD BE FINE IF WE STAY OUT OF THEIR WAY.

C'MON, WE HAVEN'T GOT MUCH TIME TO FIND THEM.

KEEP YOUR HEAD DOWN.

OOF!

FUD

I KNEW THIS WAS A BAD IDEA.

C'MON. I KNOW YOU'RE CLOSE, I CAN SMELL YA.

FINALLY.

RUCKUS?
WOLVERINE?!
NOT QUITE.
WE'RE GETTING YOU AND RAMROD OUT OF HERE.

I HOPE YOU MEAN ALIVE.
THAT'S THE PLAN, BUB. C'MON, LET'S GO FIND YOUR BUDDY.

WHAT THE HELL'S HAPPENING OUT THERE?
ONE OF THE GUARDS LET SLIP ABOUT THE TERRIGEN CLOUD AND EVERYONE'S FREAKING OUT.
YOU KNOW PRISONS. ALWAYS ONE STEP AWAY FROM A RIOT.

SOONER I'M OUT OF HERE THE BETTER.

RAMROD'S NOT HERE.
DAMMIT. WHY'S NOTHING EVER EASY?
WHERE ELSE WOULD HE BE?
HE'S GOT A CHALK FACTORY ON THE OTHER SIDE OF THE YARD. THE SMELL OF THE PRUNO IS PROBABLY PUTTING OFF YOUR NOSE.
SORRY, YOU HAVE TO LEARN THE LINGO TO GET BY HERE.
HE'S GOT A *D.I.Y. DISTILLERY* ON THE OTHER SIDE OF THE PRISON. THE ALCOHOL'S PROBABLY HIDING HIS SCENT.

SO HOW DO WE GET THERE?

UNFORTUNATELY...

...WE HAVE TO GO THROUGH THAT...

I KNEW YOU WERE GOING TO SAY THAT.

WOK
WHY ARE WE STILL DISCUSSING THIS?
WHAM
SWISH
BECAUSE THERE'S STILL TIME TO DO THE RIGHT THING.

KLK KLAK KLAK KLK KLK KLK KLAK KLK
WHAT THE HELL IS THAT?
THE GUARDS ARE GOING TO END THE RIOT.

DAMMIT. EVEN IF THEY CAN'T SEE US, WE CAN'T GET PAST THEM.
THEY CAN'T SEE US?
WELL, US. I GUESS JEAN SHOULD'VE CLOAKED YOU, TOO.
"SHOULD HAVE"?!

KLAK KLK KLK KLK KLK KLK KLK KLAK

I KNOW WHAT YOU'RE THINKING.
DON'T DO IT, LOGAN. JUST FIND ANOTHER WAY.

SCREW IT!

SNIKT!
?
KRAK
THAK
WHAT THE HELL'S GOING ON? I CAN'T SEE ANYTHING?
JUST KEEP HITTING 'TIL IT STOPS.
FUD
WHUDD
THOK
SMAAKK
AAAHHHH!

FORGE? WHAT ARE--
THE WIND CHANGED!

"THE CLOUD'S MOVING QUICKER THAN WE THOUGHT."

...YOU SEE, BRITISH LAW IS COMPLICATED, AND YOU CAN'T JUST CHANGE...
THE CLOUD IS GOING TO BE HERE SOONER THAN WE ANTICIPATED.
OKAY, DO WHATEVER YOU NEED TO DO. JUST GET THEM OUT OF THERE.

LIFE AIN'T FUN WHEN YOU DON'T HAVE A HEALING FACTOR.
WHAT THE HELL'RE YE DOIN' HERE, RUCKUS?

THEY'RE HERE TO BREAK US OUT!
NOT WITH KURT STILL UNCONSCIOUS. HE'S OUR ESCAPE PLAN.

GIVE 'IM A SNIFF AH THIS.
MEIN GOTT!
HEY, GUYS...
C'MON, KURT, WE'VE GOTTA GET OUTTA HERE.
?
WHY CAN'T I--
IT'S TOO LATE, KURT. WE MISSED OUR WINDOW.
WHERE THE HELL ARE THEY?!
I DON'T THINK WE CAN STAY HERE FOR MUCH LONGER.

OKAY, RUN!

"COME TO ENGLAND," YE SAID. "WE CAN ROB BANKS," YE SAID.
WHY THE HELL DO I LISTEN TO YE?
DON'T BLAME THIS ON ME, YOU'RE THE REASON WE GOT CAUGHT--
QUIET! I'M NOT DYING HERE WITH YOU TWO IDIOTS.

SO, HERE'S THE NEW PLAN. EVERYONE THINK THIS AS LOUDLY AS YOU CAN AND MAYBE SHE'LL HEAR US.
JEANNIE, BREAK OPEN THE WEST WALL. JEANNIE, BREAK OPEN THE WEST WALL. JEANNIE, BREAK OPEN THE WEST WALL. JEANNIE, BREAK OPEN THE WEST WALL.
I CAN HEAR SOMETHING. SOMETHING FAINT.
WHAT IS IT?
I THINK IT'S "JEANNIE, BREAK OPEN THE WEST WALL."
KRKAKAAA
BANG
KRASH!
DONE!

SWEET FREEDOM!

C'MON, JEANNIE, LET'S GO!
GIVE ME A MINUTE!

YOU KNOW, SOME OF US ACTUALLY STICK TO THE PLAN.

WE'RE OUT, STORM. EVERYONE'S SAFE.
I'M SORRY THERE WASN'T ANYTHING WE COULD DO, MS. MUNROE. SOMETIMES LIFE ISN'T FAIR--

WHAT THE HELL DO YOU MEAN THEY'RE GONE?!

YOU'RE BEHIND THIS, AREN'T YOU?!
I DON'T KNOW WHAT YOU'RE TALKING ABOUT. I'VE BEEN HERE THE WHOLE TIME.
AND YOU HAVE NO PROOF.
YOU CAN'T DO THIS TO US! WE'RE--
FZZT

I JUST DON'T GET IT. I WAS SURE I PUT IT BACK TOGETHER PROPERLY, BUT MY BRAIN'S SO FRIED...
DON'T WORRY, I'M SURE NO ONE WILL NOTICE.

ANYONE NEEDS ME, I'LL BE DRUNK SOMEWHERE.

SEE, I TOLD YOU IT WOULD ALL WORK OUT. YOU'VE JUST GOT TO TRUST ME.

YOU DIDN'T THINK WE WERE JUST GOING TO LET YOU GO FREE, DID YOU?
YOU'VE STILL GOT A SENTENCE TO SERVE.

DON'T EVEN SAY IT.

--AND TOP BRASS 'AVEN'T GOT A CLUE WHAT HAPPENED TODAY SO WE'RE GETTIN' ALL THE BLAME!

HOW ON EARTH ARE WE MEANT TO KNOW WHAT HAPPENED?! I'M NO EXPERT, AM I?
PROBABLY THAT CLOUD STUFF MADE THEM DISAPPEAR OR SOMETHIN'.

EITHER WAY, BEST IF WE STAY OUT OF THE BOSSES' WAY FOR A WHILE 'TIL WE GET BACK IN THEIR GOOD BOOKS--

?

I WON'T TELL IF YOU WON'T.

FORGE, WE HAVE A PROBLEM.

BRANDON MONTCLARE - WRITER
ROSI KÄMPE - ARTIST
IAN HERRING - COLOR ARTIST
VC's JOE CARAMAGNA - LETTERER

LOWER EAST SIDE.
AN EMPTY LOT ON YANCY STREET.
T-MINUS 5 MINUTES TO LIFTOFF.
...THIS THING WILL NEVER FLY!

WE DOING THIS OR WHAT?
WE'RE DOING THIS. WHEN I DISCOVERED YOUR WORK ON TERRIGEN I WAS BLOWN AWAY.
YOU'VE TAKEN THE RESEARCH IN DIRECTIONS NO ONE ELSE HAS...
...AND YOU SAY THE HYPOTHESES ARE BASED ON THE REVERSE-ENGINEERING OF ANCIENT KREE TECHNOLOGY?
IT'S LIKE I SAID ON THE SUBREDDIT. I'M PLANNING AN EXPEDITION TO THE RUINS OF ATTILAN. ON THE BLUE AREA OF THE MOON.
RIGHT. AND I CAN GET US AN X-MEN BLACKBIRD MODIFIED FOR SPACE FLIGHT--
MY MOON ROCKET WILL GET US THERE JUST FINE. I DO NOT HAVE TIME FOR DISTRACTIONS.
NOT ENOUGH TIME?! THE BLACKBIRD IS SUPERSONIC!
FORGE! FOR THE LAST TIME--I'M DOING THIS MY WAY.

NOT HAVING TIME IS WHAT I'M WORRIED ABOUT, LUNELLA. THE TERRIGEN CLOUD IS UNPREDICTABLE. IT CAN LAND WITHOUT WARNING--
YOU DON'T HAVE TO TELL ME ABOUT IT!
I KNOW IT KILLS MUTANTS.
BUT YOU'RE NOT A MUTANT? CEREBRO WOULD DETECT AN X-GENE...
...NO...
YOU'RE INHUMAN. EXPOSURE TO TERRIGEN WILL TRIGGER A TRANSFORMATION.
NOT WILL. IT DID. I WAS TRAPPED THE LAST TIME THE TERRIGEN CLOUD DESCENDED ON NEW YORK.
AND IT MADE YOU INTO A SUPER ENGINEER! THAT WAS MY MUTANT GIFT.
NO!
I WAS ALWAYS SMART.
THEN WHAT HAPPENED? I DON'T SEE ANY CHANGE...
IT'S COMPLICATED.
...UGH...
I SWITCH BRAINS WITH A RED TYRANNOSAURUS REX I TELEPORTED HERE FROM WHAT I THINK WAS AN ALTERNATE PAST EARTH. BASICALLY IT'S THE WORST.
I HAVE NO CONTROL OVER IT. YOU BETTER HOPE IT DOESN'T HAPPEN WHEN I'M FLYING US TO THE MOON!

VARIABLES CAN CHANGE AT ANY TIME.
YOU SHOULD ACCEPT THAT.
YOU ARE WHAT YOU ARE.
SAYS YOU!

I JUST WANT TO GET ON WITH MY LIFE.
TERRIGEN CAN'T HURT ME! NOT ANYMORE.
BUT MAYBE I CAN FIND A CURE. REVERSE MY TERRIGENESIS.
MAYBE NOT. MAYBE LUNELLA LAFAYETTE JUST SAVES SOMEONE ELSE.

MOON GIRL HAS ALREADY SAVED A LOT OF LIVES.
I SUPPORT YOUR IDEAS. EVEN THOUGH FLYING IN THIS...THIS THING... MIGHT NOT BE THE BEST IDEA YOU'VE EVER HAD...
IT'S CALLED THE MOON ROCKET.
I'M TELLING YOU--TAKE YOUR TIME. THIS MOON ROCKET IS NOWHERE CLOSE TO FLIGHT-READY.
THE MOON ROCKET.
LISTEN...YOUR HOLOGRAPHIC CLOAKING MECHANISM SEEMS TO BE KEEPING THE LOCALS AWAY. MAYBE WE SHOULD SLEEP ON IT AND COME BACK TOMORROW?
WEEEEHOOO WEEEEHOOO

WEEEEHOOO WEEEEHOOO
WHAT IS IT?
MY OLD SENSORS... IT'S THE TERRIGEN CLOUD WARNING SYSTEM.
YOU'LL BE OKAY, LUNELLA.
BUT IT'S YOU...YOU WON'T BE OKAY, FORGE. THIS IS HOW IT HAPPENED TO ME. I COULDN'T ESCAPE IT.
BUT THE TERRIGEN CLOUD WILL KILL YOU.
WE'RE SURROUNDED!
THIS WAY!

TERRIGEN!
IT'S HERE!
FAN-CANNON ISN'T HAVING ANY EFFECT. I...I DON'T HAVE ANYTHING ELSE.
I DON'T KNOW WHAT TO DO!
LUNELLA-- THIS ISN'T YOUR FAULT.
PROMISE ME YOU'LL NEVER STOP TRYING TO DEVELOP A CURE. THAT YOU'LL FINISH THE MOON ROCKET.
THAT'S IT!

WHAT?!
THE MOON ROCKET, SILLY.
NO-WHERE TO GO BUT UP!
WE'RE GOING TO BLOW THIS JOINT.
I'M TALKING 3...2...1... LIFTOFF!
YOU'LL BLOW US TO NANO-SMITHEREENS.
THEN WE'LL BOTH BE DEAD.
YOU WORRY TOO--
LOOK OUT!
SNAP!
GGGGGGGRBB!
NNGH!

OOPH!
STRAP YOURSELF IN!
LUNELLA! THE TERRIGEN WON'T HURT YOU. I CAN'T LET YOU RISK A LAUNCH JUST TO SAVE ME.
WE'VE BEEN OVER THIS, FORGE. I DO THINGS MY WAY.
THE WHOLE BLOCK COULD EXPLODE!
STOP TRYING TO JINX IT. I KNOW WHAT I'M DOING.
IGNITION
RRRMMM-BBBB
RRRRRMMMM-BB

HOUSTON STREET, WE HAVE LIFTOFF!
RMBL-RCKT
I ALWAYS DREAMED OF FLYING TO THE MOON IN A ROCKET SHIP I BUILT MYSELF.
YOU DON'T REALLY THINK WE'LL MAKE IT TO THE MOON IN THIS FLYING JUNK HEAP?
I DON'T THINK WE'RE EVEN GONNA MAKE BROOKLYN.
BUT THE VARIABLES CHANGED--
WE'LL CLEAR THE POISON CLOUD... AND KEEP MY NEW FRIEND SAFE.

ANNUAL #1 VARIANT BY RON LIM, CORY HAMSCHER & ANDREW CROSSLEY

ISSUE #15 LAYOUTS BY VICTOR IBAÑEZ WITH GUILLERMO MOGORRÓN

ISSUE #13 COVER SKETCHES BY HUMBERTO RAMOS

ISSUE #16 COVER SKETCHES BY KEN LASHLEY

ISSUE #15 COVER SKETCHES BY HUMBERTO RAMOS